£3.95

REAL NAME:

SUPER HERO NAME:

SUPER POWERS:

THIS BOOK IS THE PROPERTY OF THE SUPER HERO NAMED ABOVE. MISUSE OF THIS ANNUAL BY UNAUTHORISED PERSONNEL IS STRICTLY FORBIDDEN.

Greetings, Hero! Welcome to the hallowed ranks of the MARVEL SUPER HEROES. In this book are several stories about your fellow superhumans and mutants, so you will know how they act before you meet them on your OWN adventures!

Cover by Martin Griffiths Inks by Simon Coleby Colour by John Burns
Super hero Double Spread by Jeff Anderson
Editor and Designer: John Freeman

MARVEL SUPER HEROES ANNUAL 1989 Published by MARVEL COMICS LTD., a New World company, 23 Redan Place, London W2 4SA. SPIDER-MAN AND HIS AMAZING FRIENDS material © 1981, Marvel Entertainments Group Inc. FANTASTIC FOUR material © 1981 Marvel Entertainments Group Inc. UNCANNY X-MEN material © 1987 Marvel Entertainments Group Inc. INCREDIBLE HULK material © 1987 Marvel Entertainments Group Inc. All other material © Marvel Comics Ltd. 1988. All rights reserved. Printed in Italy. No similarity between any of the names, characters, persons and/or institutions in this publication with those of any living or dead person or institution is intended. Any such similarity which may exist is purely coincidental. SPIDER-MAN, FIRESTAR, ICEMAN, THE FANTASTIC FOUR, DOCTOR STRANGE, THE UNCANNY X-MEN, THE INCREDIBLE HULK and prominent characters featured in this annual, and the distinctive likenesses thereof, are trademarks of Marvel Entertainments Group Inc.

Even when you're a superhero, it often pays to work as a team to beat a dangerous enemy! THE AMAZING SPIDERMAN, FIRESTAR and ICEMAN work together in this story when they face the menace of The Green Goblin!

Stan Lee PRESENTS:

SPIDER-MAN AND HIS AMAZING FRIENDS! ™

SPIDER-MAN... BITTEN BY A RADIOACTIVE SPIDER, PETER PARKER GAINED ITS PROPORTIONATE STRENGTH AND SPEED, BECOMING A HUMAN SPIDER!

FIRE-STAR... BORN WITH THE ABILITY TO CONTROL HEAT IN ALL OF ITS FORMS, ANGELICA JONES IS THE HOTTEST LITTLE NUMBER OF ALL!

ICEMAN... POSSESSING THE FREEZING POWER OF SUB-ZERO COLD, BOBBY DRAKE MAKES THE UNDERWORLD SHIVER IN FEAR!

AND INTRODUCING THE LOVABLE... MS. LION!

HI THERE, TRUE BELIEVER! WE THOUGHT YOU'D GET A BIG KICK OUT OF THIS COLOURFUL ADAPTATION OF OUR ALL-NEW SPIDER-MAN AND HIS AMAZING FRIENDS CARTOON SHOW! THE MAIN CHARACTERS AND STORY MAY SEEM DELIGHTFULLY DIFFERENT FROM WHAT YOU'RE USED TO SEEING IN OUR NORMAL COLOUR COMICS, BUT THIS IS FOR THE FUN OF IT! SO HANG LOOSE AND ENJOY!

THE TRIUMPH OF THE GREEN GOBLIN!

ADAPTED FROM THE ORIGINAL SCREENPLAY BY DENNIS MARKS!
PENCILS--DAN SPIEGLE • INKS--VINCENT COLLETTA • LETTERS--JIM NOVAK
COLOURS--BOB SHAREN • EDITOR--TOM DEFALCO • EDITOR-IN-CHIEF--JIM SHOOTER

THUNDER ROCKS THE SKY! LIGHTNING SEARS THE HEAVENS!

BUFFETED BY SAVAGE WINDS, A SMALL PRIVATE PLANE STRUGGLES DESPERATELY AGAINST THE STORM...

I'M SORRY I MADE YOU FLY IN THIS WEATHER--

--BUT I JUST HAD TO GET AWAY FROM THE SANITARIUM AS SOON AS POSSIBLE!

DON'T WORRY, MR. OSBORN! WE'LL MAKE IT!

I HOPE!

AT LAST--AFTER THREE LONG YEARS-- THE DOCTORS SAY I'M CURED! I CAN GO BACK TO MY WORK IN CHEMICAL RESEARCH! I CAN BE NORMAN OSBORN AGAIN... NOT THAT OTHER CREATURE THEY SAY I TURN INTO...

"I'VE HAD AMNESIA--AND DON'T REMEMBER ANY OF THIS -- BUT ACCORDING TO THE DOCTORS, MY PROBLEMS ALL STARTED ONE DAY WHILE I WAS WORKING IN MY CHEMICAL FACTORY-- PERFECTING A NEW FORMULA...

"SUDDENLY, SOMETHING WENT WRONG, AND...

KA-BOOM

"THE ACCIDENT GAVE ME SUPER-HUMAN POWERS, AND MY NEW IDENTITY AS... THE GREEN GOBLIN!"

JUST THEN, NORMAN OSBORN'S THOUGHTS ARE SHATTERED AS...

MR. OSBORN! WE'VE GOT PROBLEMS!

WHAT IS IT? WHAT'S WRONG?

LIGHTNING IS STRIKING THE SHIP!

WE'VE LOST POWER IN BOTH ENGINES!

WE MUST BAIL OUT!

THEN, SECONDS LATER...

RAVAGED BY THE RAGING STORM, THE PARACHUTES DROP QUICKLY...

OH, NO! OSBORN LANDED PRETTY HARD! LOOKS LIKE HE HIT HIS HEAD!

HOPE HE'S ALRIGHT!

BUT...

CURED? THE FOOLS THINK I'M CURED!

NEVER!

THE GREEN GOBLIN LIVES AGAIN!

7

MEANWHILE, IN **SHADY GLEN**--A SMALL SUBURBAN COLLEGE TOWN LOCATED OUTSIDE NEW YORK CITY--IS AUNT MAY'S BOARDING HOUSE...

AUNT MAY'S

GRRR!

GRRR!

YIPES! I SCARED MYSELF!

LOOK AT MS. LION PLAYING IN FRONT OF THE MIRROR!

MS. LION! COME OUT AND SEE THE GIRLS IN THEIR COSTUMES! THEY'RE GOING TO THE EASTERN STATE UNIVERSITY SUPER HERO PARTY!

AUNT MAY, WHERE ARE BOBBY DRAKE AND PETER PARKER? I'M ALMOST READY TO LEAVE WITHOUT THEM!

I'M SURE THEY'LL BE HERE SOON!

ANGELICA JONES! WHY DID YOU DECIDE TO GO DRESSED LIKE THAT AWFUL SPIDER-WOMAN?

IT'S A PRIVATE JOKE BETWEEN YOUR NEPHEW PETER AND ME, AUNT MAY!

NOBODY'S COMPLIMENTED MY COSTUME-- **MEDUSA**, THE INHUMAN WITH LIVING HAIR!

NORMA OSBORN, YOU LOOK STUNNING!

THE POOR GIRL! I'M CERTAIN SHE STILL MISSES HER UNCLE WHO WAS SENT AWAY TO THE SANITARIUM!

8

"-- THERE ARE SOME SUPER VILLAINS HERE, TOO!"

THE GREEN GOBLIN!

TWO OF THEM! THEY'RE FLYING ON WIRES!

MY SPIDER-SENSE IS WARNING ME OF DANGER!

THESE GOBLINS MAY BE FAKE, BUT SOMETHING'S MAKING ME TINGLE!

ER... EXCUSE ME, ANGELICA, I--UH-HAVE TO BE GOING!

WELL, OF ALL THE NERVE--!

FINDING A NEARBY DESERTED CLASSROOM, PETER PARKER UNDERGOES A STARTLING TRANSFORMATION...

I DITCHED THAT CHEAP, DIME-STORE SPIDER-MAN COSTUME--AND CHANGED INTO THE REAL THING 'CAUSE--

--IT'S WEB-SPINNING TIME!

THWIP

10

MY SPIDER-SENSE IS DIRECTING ME TOWARD THE OSBORN BUILDING!

I'LL JUST SWING IN THAT TOP FLOOR WINDOW AND FIND OUT WHY!

BUT NO SOONER DOES THE WONDROUS WEB-SWINGER ENTER THE BUILDING, THEN HE FINDS HIMSELF UNDER ATTACK...

ZZIT

ZZIT

ZZIT

USING HIS AMAZING SPIDER-SPEED AND AGILITY, HE AVOIDS HARM--

--UNTIL...

THERE! I KNEW YOU COULDN'T AVOID MY RAY-BLASTS FOREVER!

LATER, WHEN CONSCIOUSNESS RETURNS TO THE DAZED WALL-CRAWLER...

OH, NO!

YES, SPIDER-MAN! YOU ARE AT THE MERCY OF THE GREEN GOBLIN!

AND YOU ALREADY KNOW THAT I DON'T HAVE ANY MERCY!

WHEN I WAS NORMAN OSBORN, CAPTAIN OF INDUSTRY, I DONATED THIS LAB TO THE COLLEGE--AND HID MY GREATEST TREASURE HERE--

-- THE FORMULA THAT CHANGED ME INTO THE GREEN GOBLIN!

"WITH IT, I CAN HAVE THE ULTIMATE REVENGE! MY FORMULA WILL MAKE EVERYONE IN NEW YORK LOOK UGLY, GROTESQUE AND HORRIBLE... *LIKE ME!*"

TURNING AWAY FROM SPIDER-MAN, THE GREEN GOBLIN ATTEMPTS TO OPEN THE LOCKED VAULT...

THIS GOBLIN GRENADE OF LIQUID NITROGEN WILL FREEZE THE VAULT TO TWO HUNDRED DEGREES BELOW ZERO--

--SO THAT IT CAN BE SHATTERED WITH A SINGLE BLOW!

WAP

MEANWHILE, AT THE SUPER HERO PARTY...

PETER'S BEEN GONE AN AWFULLY LONG TIME!

HEY, ANGELICA! LET'S DANCE!

I'D BETTER SEE WHAT'S KEEPING HIM!

HOW ABOUT IT, ANGELICA? ANGELICA--!

WELL, EX-CUUUSE ME!

AT THAT MOMENT...

IT'S NOT HERE!

MY FORMULA IS GONE!

STILL GROGGY! CAN HARDLY MOVE--CAN'T EVEN SPEAK!

OF COURSE! MY NIECE-- NORMA OSBORN--IS A STUDENT HERE!

SHE'LL KNOW WHERE THE FORMULA HAS BEEN HIDDEN!

WAIT! SOME- ONE'S OUT IN THE HALLWAY!

PETER--?

IN THE HALL...

I NOTICED THE LIGHT IN THIS BUILDING--AND I'VE LOOKED EVERYWHERE ELSE FOR PETER!

PETER, ARE YOU HERE?

HA! HA! HA! WONDERFUL! I CAN USE YOUR OWN FRIEND TO DO MY DIRTY WORK --AND DESTROY YOU!

AND SO, SECONDS LATER...

WHEN THAT YOUNG LADY OPENS THE DOOR-- SHE'LL GET A CHILLING RECEPTION! THE LIQUID NITROGEN IN THAT GOBLIN GRENADE WILL FREEZE YOU BOTH!

GOODBYE, SPIDER-MAN... FOREVER!

13

THERE'S SOMETHING WRONG HERE!

SPIDER-WOMAN, YOU'RE GREAT! BUT YOU'RE NOT ME...

SUDDENLY, INTENSE WAVES OF MUTANT-HEAT RADIATE FROM THE BODY OF ANGELICA JONES...

IF I'M GOING TO FACE TROUBLE, I'LL DO IT AS--

--FIRE-STAR!

AND THEN...

PETER, I'M COMING IN!

OH, NO!

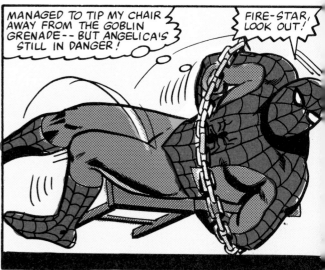

MANAGED TO TIP MY CHAIR AWAY FROM THE GOBLIN GRENADE-- BUT ANGELICA'S STILL IN DANGER!

FIRE-STAR, LOOK OUT!

REACTING INSTANTLY, FIRE-STAR RAISES HER BODY TEMPERATURE TO AN INCREDIBLE INTENSITY, FORMING A PROTECTIVE HEAT-SHIELD, JUST AS THE DEADLY GOBLIN GRENADE RELEASES ITS FREEZING MIST...

BUT THEN...

SPIDEY, I'M LOSING POWER! I CAN'T HOLD THE LIQUID NITROGEN OFF MUCH LONGER!

IT'S EATING THROUGH MY HEAT SHIELD! I'LL CRYSTALLIZE!

DON'T SWEAT IT, HOTSTUFF! YOUR HEAT HELPED TO REVIVE ME!

AND NOW THAT I'M FREE--

--I'LL JUST USE MY WEBBING TO SEAL THAT CANISTER'S NOZZLE!

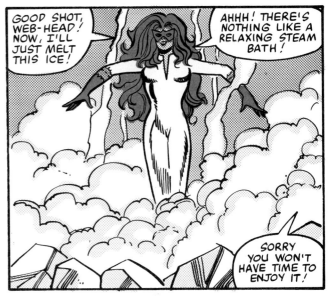

GOOD SHOT, WEB-HEAD! NOW, I'LL JUST MELT THIS ICE!

AHHH! THERE'S NOTHING LIKE A RELAXING STEAM BATH!

SORRY YOU WON'T HAVE TIME TO ENJOY IT!

WE HAVE TO GET BACK TO THE DANCE! NORMAN OSBORN'S BECOME THE GREEN GOBLIN AGAIN!

HE'S REALLY FLIPPED OUT THIS TIME! THAT GOBLIN GET-UP IS ONLY A COSTUME, BUT HE THINKS IT'S FOR REAL!

"--AND HE'S AFTER HIS NIECE NORMA!"

-- SO THE PROFESSOR SAID, "MR. DRAKE, WHAT'S C_6H_5OH?" AND I SAID, "I'M NOT SURE, BUT IT'S RIGHT ON THE TIP OF MY TONGUE."

AND HE SAID, "WELL YOU BETTER SPIT IT OUT, 'CAUSE THAT'S CARBOLIC ACID!"

OH, BOBBY! YOU'RE SO SILLY!

SUDDENLY, A GREEN-GARBED FIGURE STREAKS INTO VIEW, THEN...

NORMA OSBORN? MAY I HAVE THE NEXT DANCE?

WHAT THE--?

WOW! THAT STUDENT REALLY RIGGED UP THOSE WIRES SO YOU CAN'T-- WIRES??? WE'RE OUTSIDE!

THAT MUST HAVE BEEN--

-- THE REAL GREEN GOBLIN!

16

THEN, AFTER ALL HAS BEEN EXPLAINED TO BOBBY DRAKE...

SO! THE GREEN GOBLIN'S BACK--AND HE HAS NORMA!

WE'D BETTER GET HER BACK! I'LL JUST USE MY MUTANT-POWERS TO FREEZE THE MOISTURE IN THE AIR, AND BECOME--

--THE ICEMAN!

SECONDS LATER...

WE'LL FIND THE GOBLIN FASTER IF WE SPLIT UP! I'LL TRY OSBORN'S OLD FACTORY!

I'LL TAKE THE HEAD-QUARTERS OF OSBORN INDUSTRIES!

I'LL CHECK NORMA'S HOME!

POOR NORMA! SHE DOESN'T EVEN KNOW THAT HER UNCLE IS THE GREEN GOBLIN!

RAISING HER BODY TEMPERA-TURE UNTIL IT IS LIGHTER THAN AIR, FIRE-STAR RIDES THE THERMAL AIR CURRENTS...

... WHILE HER COLD COMPATRIOT RACES THROUGH THE CITY ON AN ICE-SLED!

THE GOBLIN'S PLANNING TO USE A FORMULA THAT'LL CHANGE EVERYBODY IN THE CITY INTO UGLY LITTLE GREEN CREATURES!

FOR SPIDEY, THAT WOULD BE AN IM-PROVEMENT!

17

SOMETIME LATER...

PLEASE... DON'T HURT ME...

...I DID AS YOU ASKED. I SHOWED YOU WHERE THEY KEPT MY UNCLE'S FORMULA!

HOW CAN I TELL IF THE FORMULA WORKS -- IF I DON'T TEST IT? TAKE ONE LITTLE SIP--

NO! I DON'T WANT TO LOOK-- LIKE --LIKE--

--LIKE ME? SOON, EVERYONE WILL LOOK LIKE ME!

DRINK!

NO!

LOOKS LIKE I LUCKED-OUT! I FOUND THE GOBLIN FIRST --AND NORMA'S ALRIGHT!

YOU AGAIN! YOU MEDDLESOME FOOL!

18

GOBLIN, I CAN ALWAYS COUNT ON YOU FOR SNAPPY DIALOGUE!

I'LL TAKE THAT BEAKER!

THWIPP

THERE! THAT SHOULD END YOUR PLAN TO TURN THIS TOWN INTO GOBLIN CITY!

KER-ASH

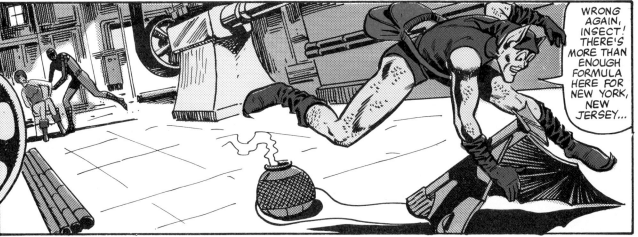

WRONG AGAIN, INSECT! THERE'S MORE THAN ENOUGH FORMULA HERE FOR NEW YORK, NEW JERSEY...

...PHILADELPHIA, WASHINGTON...

THERE'S SOMETHING SO FAMILIAR ABOUT HIM!...

SORRY, NORMA, BUT I CAN'T STAY AND CHAT!

THERE'S NO TELLING WHAT DAMAGE HE COULD DO WITH THAT FORMULA!

I GOTTA STOP THE GOBLIN BEFORE HE REACHES ANAHEIM, AZUZA, AND CUCAMONGA!

YA-HOO! I SNAGGED HIS BAT-SLED!

BUT SPIDER-MAN'S AMAZING ACCURACY PROVES TO BE HIS UNDOING...

YEEOOOWWW!

YOU'VE DOOMED YOURSELF, FOOL!

I'LL USE CENTRIFUGAL FORCE TO GET RID OF YOU!

I'LL KEEP SPINNING IN A CIRCLE-- MOVING FASTER AND FASTER--

"--UNTIL THE PRESSURE BECOMES TOO GREAT! GOODBYE, SPIDER-MAN!"

COULDN'T HOLD ON ANY LONGER! HAD TO LET GO!

20

MEANWHILE...

HA! HA! HA!

CITY RESERVOIR

I WIN! THE GREEN GOBLIN TRIUMPHS AT LAST!

BY TOMORROW, EVERYBODY IN THE CITY WILL BE TRANSFORMED INTO UGLY LITTLE GREEN CREATURES ...LIKE ME!

SORRY, BUT YOU'RE NOT MY TYPE!

THE TROUBLESOME TRIO! YOU'RE TOO LATE! I'VE ALREADY POISONED THE WATER!

NOTHING CAN STOP ME NOW!

WE'LL SEE ABOUT THAT!

=WHOOPS= HERE WE GO AGAIN!

22

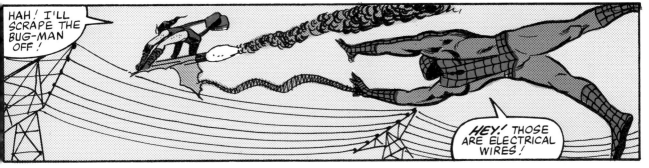

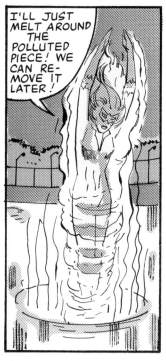

I'LL JUST MELT AROUND THE POLLUTED PIECE! WE CAN RE-MOVE IT LATER!

MEANWHILE...

WH-WHAT HAPPENED? MY PLANE WAS IN A STORM, AND I BAILED OUT...

HE DOESN'T REMEMBER ANY OF THIS! HE'S NORMAN OSBORN AGAIN!

AND SO...

OSBORN WILL BE RETURNED TO THE SANITARIUM! MAYBE THIS TIME THEY CAN CURE HIM FOR GOOD!

MAYBE...

WE'LL DROP THIS IN THE SEWER!

SOMETIME LATER, AT AUNT MAY'S BOARDING HOUSE...

AND THEN, SPIDER-MAN SAVED ME! HE'S SO WONDER-FUL!

IF YOU LIKE CRAWLY, BUGGY GUYS...

...WHO ARE SWELLED-HEADED, CONCEITED, AND OVER-BEARING!

MS. LION, WHAT DO YOU THINK OF SPIDER-MAN?

ME?

I LOVE HIM!

THE END

24

SPOT THE MISTAKE

A super hero has to be a modern Sherlock Holmes to beat some criminals! There are at least 12 mistakes in this drawing. Can you spot them all?

Answers on Page 92!

THE FANTASTIC FOUR

FANTASTIC FOUR FACT FILE

On a spaceflight in a test rocket, Reed Richards, Ben Grimm, Sue and Johnny Storm were exposed to mysterious cosmic rays. The foursome soon discovered that their bodies had been changed by the rays, so Reed became a man of rubber, MR FANTASTIC, Ben Grimm became the rock-like THING, while Sue became the INVISIBLE GIRL. As for Johnny, he became the HUMAN TORCH. Together they decided to fight evil as THE FANTASTIC FOUR.

Since that fateful spaceflight, Sue has married Reed Richards and they now have a son called Franklin. The Fantastic Four count many Marvel Superheroes as their friends, some who have been helped by Reed's brilliant inventions. These friends include Spider-man, Captain America, Doctor Strange, Thor and many more!

Once more, in this story, you can see why superheroes often work together as a group to defeat their enemies. The FANTASTIC FOUR are a perfect example of teamwork — teamwork which has taken years of practice and experience and has made them the formidable force against evil that they are today!

STan Lee PRESENTS: THE FANTASTIC FOUR!®

JOHN BYRNE WORDS & PICTURES / **BJORN HEYN** INKS / **JIM NOVAK** LETTERS / **GLYNIS WEIN** COLOURS / **JIM SALICRUP** EDITOR / **JIM SHOOTER** EDITOR-IN-CHIEF

BACK TO THE BASICS!

THE FANTASTIC FOUR -- MY OLD AND MUCH VAUNTED FOES -- SHALL SOON LEARN WHO IS TRULY MOST POWERFUL!

SOON I SHALL DESTROY THEM AS EASILY AS I HAVE CONJURED THEIR IMAGES.

THE ARCANE POTIONS FILL THE AIR WITH THEIR NOXIOUS FUMES, AND CANDLE LIGHT GLIMMERS IN EYES NOT A LITTLE MAD.

HE IS CALLED *DIABLO*, AND HE IS MASTER OF THE ARTS ALCHEMICAL.

AND YOU, MY SMALL ONES, GARNERED FROM THE FOUR FAR CORNERS OF THE EARTH, YOU SHALL BE MY INSTRUMENTS.

THROUGH YOU THE FANTASTIC FOUR WILL MEET THEIR FINAL, IRREVOCABLE DEFEAT!

BUT EVEN AS DIABLO CACKLES AT HIS ANTICIPATED VICTORY...

MR. OLBAID! MR. OLBAID, YOU OPEN THIS DOOR!

UH-- YES, MRS. MULLIGAN? IS THERE SOME PROBLEM?

WHAT ARE THOSE HORRIBLE SMELLS? ARE YOU COOKING IN YOUR ROOM, MR. OLBAID?

OH, NO, MRS. MULLIGAN! I WOULDN'T THINK OF SUCH A THING!

WELL... YOU SEE THAT YOU DON'T!

AND, AS THE MEEK LITTLE MAN CLOSES THE DOOR...

VILE WOMAN! ALWAYS PRYING! FORCING ME TO WASTE PRECIOUS POTIONS ON MASKING SPELLS...

BUT SOON SHE WILL PAY! SOON SHE AND ALL HER SNIVELLING, SNOOPING ILK WILL BE CRUSHED BENEATH MY HEEL...

YES-- VERY SOON.

HE MOVES QUICKLY NOW, LONG, TAPERED FINGERS SPRINKLING POWDERS AND CRUSHED HERBS, LIPS MOVING TO THE SILENT CADENCE OF LONG FORGOTTEN TONGUES...

ARISE NOW, MY LITTLE ONES! SEND FORTH YOUR PRIMAL SPIRITS. SEEK OUT OUR ENEMIES...

...CRUSH THE FANTASTIC FOUR!

AND ON THAT OMINOUS NOTE, WE TURN OUR GAZE NORTHWARDS, TO ONE OF MANHATTAN'S MOST EXCLUSIVE BEAUTY SALONS...

AND ONE OF ITS MOST FAMOUS CLIENTS, SUSAN STORM RICHARDS, *THE INVISIBLE GIRL*...

SUZIE, BABY, THIS NEW CUT IS GONNA MAKE YOU LOOK TWENTY YEARS YOUNGER!

WONDERFUL, MILO, I'M SURE MY HUSBAND WILL LOVE BEING MARRIED TO A CHILD!

OOH, AREN'T WE JUST *TOO* CUTTING TODAY! HERE, LET ME COMB IT OUT AND YOU'LL SEE FOR YOURSELF!

ISN'T THE VERONICA LAKE LOOK A TRIFLE *PASSÉ*, MILO?

JUST THEN...

OH, MISTER TINDOLINI, LOOK! SOMETHING'S HAPPENING TO THE CONSTRUCTION SITE OUT ON THE STREET!

WEIRD! WHAT COULD MAKE ALL THOSE ROCKS AND DIRT FLY INTO THE AIR LIKE THAT?

WHAT INDEED...

HEAR ME, HUMANS!

I AM COME FOR SHE WHO IS THE INVISIBLE GIRL!

WOE BETIDE THOSE WHO STAND IN MY WAY!

THAT THING IS AFTER ME?! MILO, THIS MAY BE MORE THAN I CAN HANDLE ON MY OWN, WILL YOU CALL MY...

SORRY, SUZIE! YOU HEARD WHAT THAT THING SAID! YOU'RE ON YOUR OWN!

WELL, THANK YOU MR. TINDOLINI! GOOD THING REED SUGGESTED I PRACTICE CONTROL OF MY INVISIBILITY POWERS...

BY KEEPING MY UNIFORM INVISIBLE UNDER MY STREET CLOTHES, NOW I CAN SHED MY OUTER GARMENTS WITHOUT MAKING THE FRONT PAGE OF THE NATIONAL ENQUIRER!

SUSAN RICHARDS, I AM COME FOR YOU!

KR-RESH

IT'S SO HUGE! SO POWERFUL!

IN SOME WAYS, IT RE- MINDS ME OF THE THING!

SURRENDER AND YOUR DEATH SHALL BE MERCIFUL AND QUICK!

TURNING INVISIBLE WILL AVAIL YOU NOUGHT!

MAYBE NOT, TALL, DARK AND UGLY...

BUT IF I CAN JUST REACH MY PURSE AND F.F. SIGNAL FLARE-GUN...

FOOLISH FEMALE! YOUR POWERS ARE AS NOTHING AGAINST ME...

NO!

HE'S FILLING THE ROOM WITH FLYING, CLINGING DIRT-- COATING ME...

AND IT'S HARDENING... LIKE CEMENT... I... CAN'T... MOVE...

ELSEWHERE, A FEW SHORT BLOCKS TO THE SOUTH, AND A FEW MINUTES AGO, A MATINEE CROWD LEAVES A BROADWAY THEATRE...

ELEPHANT MAN

ELEPHANT MAN

TAXI

...LARGELY UNAWARE OF TWO CELEBRITIES IN THEIR MIDST...

...BEN GRIMM, THE INCREDIBLY POWERFUL *THING*, AND HIS LADY LOVE, FAMED BLIND SCULPTRESS *ALICIA MASTERS*.

OH, BEN, WASN'T THAT A WONDERFUL PLAY? SO TERRIBLY SAD AND YET SO BEAUTIFUL.

YEAH, IT ⋛SNIF⋚ HAD ITS MOMENTS...

AW, CRUMBS! WHAT A LOUSY TIME FER IT TO START RAININ'!

RAINING? WHAT ARE YOU TALKING ABOUT?

IT ISN'T RAINING, BEN!

HOLY COW, SHE'S RIGHT! THE REST OF THE STREET IS BONE DRY! IT'S ONLY RAININ' ON ME!

BEN? BEN, WHAT IS IT? WHAT'S HAPPENING?

BEFORE THE STARTLED THING CAN ANSWER, THE "RAIN" CHANGES TO SOMETHING FAR WORSE...

GLUB!

A BUBBLE OF WATER! IT'S ALL AROUND ME-- MOVIN' WHEN I MOVE-- I'LL *DROWN* UNLESS...

BEN! PLEASE! WHAT'S WRONG? WHY DON'T YOU ANSWER?

I WAS BREATHIN' OUT WHEN THIS THING HIT ME-- NO MORE'N A COUPLA SECONDS OF AIR LEFT...!

GOTTA KEEP CALM-- IF I PANIC I'M DONE FOR!

MAYBE-- IF I DIG UP THE SIDEWALK I CAN FIND AIR-- FIND A WAY OUT...

S'NO GOOD! NO MATTER HOW DEEP I GO THIS BLASTED WATER BUBBLE'S GONNA STAY RIGHT WITH ME...!

BUT THERE'S GOTTA BE A WAY OUT, THERE'S GOTTA!

GETTIN' HARD TO THINK-- TO CONCENTRATE...

MY LUNGS FEEL LIKE THEY'RE ABOUT TA BURST... NO MORE AIR... NO MORE...

AND, AS A BLOOD RED VEIL BEGINS TO DRAW CLOSED ACROSS THE THING'S BRAIN...

...HIGH IN THE AIR OVER NEW YORK'S LEGENDARY CENTRAL PARK...

...A BRIGHT RED COMET RESOLVES ITSELF INTO THE SHAPE OF A MAN--A MAN NAMED JOHNNY STORM...

...THE HUMAN TORCH!

THERE SHE IS!

AT HIS UNSPOKEN COMMAND THE TORCH'S FLAME DIMINISHES, AND HE DROPS TOWARDS THE PARK...

BETTER FLAME OFF OUT OF SIGHT. I DON'T KNOW WHY MY FLAME UPSETS FRANKIE SO MUCH...

BUT IT'S ENOUGH TO KNOW THAT IT DOES. SO, EXIT ONE HIGH-FLYING SUPER HERO...

ENTER ONE LOVE-STRUCK YOUNG MAN. FRANKIE? FRANKIE RAYE?

JOHNNY!

I HALF EXPECTED YOU TO COME SWOOPING DOWN, BLAZING LIKE A BONFIRE!

NO... I MAY BE A LITTLE THICK-HEADED AT TIMES, BUT EVEN I GET THE MESSAGE SOONER OR LATER.

I'M A LITTLE SURPRISED YOU AGREED TO SEE ME, THOUGH.

WHY NOT?

AFTER ALL WE CAME DANGEROUSLY CLOSE TO MEANING SOMETHING TO EACH OTHER...

32

"DANGEROUSLY CLOSE?" IS THAT ALL YOU CAN SAY? I WAS READY TO REWRITE MY WHOLE LIFE FOR YOU. READY TO QUIT THE F.F. READY TO GIVE UP BEING THE HUMAN TORCH.

DOESN'T THAT TELL YOU HOW I FEEL ABOUT YOU?

JOHNNY, PLEASE -- THERE'S MORE TO IT THAN THAT ...SO MUCH MORE.

HOW CAN I MAKE YOU UNDERSTAND? YOU DON'T *KNOW* ME. YOU DON'T KNOW WHO -- OR WHAT -- I AM.

ISN'T IT ENOUGH TO KNOW I LOVE YOU, FRANKIE? WHAT MORE DO I...

BUT, BEFORE THE TORCH CAN FINISH...

WHAT THE...? WHAT'S GOING ON WITH THE WIND?

IT'S...IT'S LIKE A TORNADO BLOWING UP ALL OF A...

JOHNNY!

HOLY-- IT *IS* A TORNADO! A MINIATURE TORNADO SNATCHING US UP INTO THE AIR!

WHOOF! THE WIND-- IT'S DROPPED ME!

BUT IT'S STILL GOT JOHNNY!

THE WIND'S-- WHIRLING ME SO FAST-- I CAN'T FLAME-ON. I CAN'T SAVE MYSELF!

DROPPING TOWARDS THOSE ROCKS...

A BONE-JARRING IMPACT, AND THE TORCH SLUMPS INTO SEMI-CONSCIOUSNESS...

AND AS HE DOES THE SWIRLING WINDS SHRINK TO A VAGUELY HUMAN SHAPE!

34

NO, FOOLISH MORTAL! I AM NOT THE HUMAN TORCH! I AM HE WHO IS THE *LIVING FLAME!*

AND I AM YOUR DEATH, REED RICHARDS!

LIVING FLAME?

IT'S SOME KIND OF ELEMENTAL FIRE CREATURE -- BUT WHO HAS THE ABILITY TO CREATE SUCH A THING?

AND AS THE GIANT INTELLECT OF THE MAN CALLED *MR. FANTASTIC* PONDERS THAT QUESTION...

OUTSIDE, A WALL OF LIVING FIRE SURROUNDS THE UPPER FLOORS OF THE BAXTER BUILDING...

THE TEMPERATURE IS BECOMING TOO HIGH --SOON IT WILL BE INTOLERABLE.

YOUR PUNY ATTEMPTS TO EVADE ME WILL AVAIL YOU NOUGHT, RICHARDS. SOON YOU WILL DIE, AS MY COUNTERPARTS ARE EVEN NOW DESTROYING YOUR PARTNERS.

WHAT? THE OTHERS ARE IN DANGER TOO?

I'VE GOT TO REACH THEM -- TO SEE WHAT KIND OF MENACE THEY FACE -- PERHAPS FIND A CLUE TO DEFEATING THIS THREAT...

WITH HARDLY A SECOND'S THOUGHT TO HIS OWN SAFETY, REED RICHARDS LAUNCHES HIMSELF THROUGH THE SURROUNDING FLAMES...

...AND PLUNGING THROUGH THE COOL OUTSIDE AIR TOWARDS THE ROOFTOPS BELOW.

THAT WAS TOO CLOSE! ONLY MY SPEED SAVED ME FROM SERIOUS INJURY!

35

AT THE LAST POSSIBLE MOMENT...

...RIDING THE SLIGHT, SLUGGISH BREEZES THAT WAFT THROUGH THE HEAVY CITY AIR.

...THE INCREDIBLY ELASTIC BODY OF MR. FANTASTIC SNAPS OUT LIKE A GREAT SAIL...

THAT THING WILL BE AFTER ME MOMENTARILY. I MUST LURE IT AWAY FROM THE SURROUNDING BUILDINGS. ONE STRAY FLAME AND HALF THE CITY COULD BE GUTTED. BUT, WHERE...?

THE PARK! OF COURSE!

IT'S A WIDE OPEN SPACE, AND THE NEW SPRING LEAVES ARE TOO DAMP TO CREATE MUCH OF A FIRE THREAT...

BUT-- FLYING ISN'T WHAT ONE WOULD CALL MY FORTE-- AND THERE'S HARDLY ANY UPLIFT...

HIS BODY ACHING AS HE STRUGGLES TO MANOEUVRE, REED GLIDES OVER CENTRAL PARK...

...AND HIS FIERY PURSUER IS BUT SECONDS BEHIND!

PROFESSOR RICHARDS! HELP! OH, PLEASE HELP!

IT'S THE GIRL JOHNNY SAID HE WAS MEETING. FRANKIE... SOMETHING...

FRANKIE, WHERE'S JOHNNY? IS HE...

HE'S OVER BEYOND THOSE ROCKS. OH, HURRY PLEASE. THERE'S SOME KIND OF.... OF WIND THING...

I THINK IT'S KILLING HIM!

"WIND THING?" THEN MY FIRST ANALYSIS WAS CORRECT. OUR ATTACKERS ARE EMBODIMENTS OF THE FOUR ELEMENTS. FIRE ATTACKED ME. NOW AIR IS ATTACKING JOHNNY.

EARTH AND WATER MUST BE AFTER BEN AND SUE. BUT-- WHICH TO WHICH?

NO TIME TO WORRY ABOUT THAT NOW!

JOHNNY! FLAME ON IF YOU CAN! GET CLEAR!

REED!

RICHARDS! BUT MY FIERY BROTHER SHOULD HAVE FINISHED YOU BY NOW!

36

NOW, I SIMPLY PRETEND TO FLEE, AND HOPEFULLY THE OVERCONFIDENCE OF THESE CREATURES WILL SET THE STAGE FOR THEIR UNDOING.

FLEE IF YOU WISH, RICHARDS.

MY FIERY SIBLING MAY HAVE FAILED, BUT I SHALL PREVAIL!

AND, AS MR. FANTASTIC ALLOWS HIMSELF A DISCRETE, GRIM SMILE...

A FEW BLOCKS AWAY AT TINDOLINI'S TONSORIAL PALACE...

THE INVISIBLE GIRL HAS BEEN ENCASED IN SOLIDIFIED EARTH FOR LESS THAN FIVE SECONDS WHEN...

I DID IT! BY EXPANDING MY INVISIBLE FORCE FIELD WITHIN THE DIRT, I'VE FREED MYSELF!

ONLY FOR A MOMENT, SUSAN RICHARDS, YOUR ACTIONS BUT PROLONG YOUR FINAL AGONY!

MAYBE, BUT THEY ALSO ALLOW ME BREATHING SPACE...

...BY GENERATING A FORCE-FIELD BUBBLE TO HOLD YOU BACK, AND PROPEL MYSELF INTO THE STREET!

NOW, WITHOUT THE RESTRICTIONS OF BEING INSIDE A BUILDING, I CAN USE MY POWER TO BEST ADVANTAGE.

AND, SINCE MY POWER ISN'T MUCH MORE THAN DEFENSIVE AGAINST BRUTE FORCE LIKE THIS...

...THAT MEANS FINDING SOMEONE BETTER EQUIPPED TO FIGHT THIS MONSTER...

...THE THING!

PUSHING MYSELF OUT OF THE STORE LIKE THAT WAS AN INSPIRATION!

I'VE NEVER THOUGHT TO USE MY FORCE-FIELD AS A MEANS OF TRANSPORTATION BEFORE, BUT AS LONG AS I'M CAREFUL...

...I SHOULD BE ABLE TO TRAVEL IN MUCH THE SAME WAY THE ICE-MAN USES HIS ICE-SLIDES. *

NOW, WHAT THEATRE DID BEN SAY HE WAS TAKING ALICIA TO?

*YOU SAW ICE-MAN'S POWERS IN THE LAST STORY

MEANWHILE... I'VE HAD IT -- NO MORE BREATH IN MY LUNGS -- MIGHT AS WELL GIVE...

WAIT... THAT SPORTS STORE... WITH SCUBA* GEAR!

*SELF-CONTAINED UNDERWATER BREATHING APPARATUS

SUMMONING HIS FINAL IOTA OF STRENGTH, THE THING STAGGERS BLINDLY TOWARDS THE SPORTING GOODS SHOP...

HERE, JAN, PUT THIS TANK ON THE...

HOLEE...!

UNABLE TO SPEAK, TOO NEAR TOTALLY COLLAPSING TO COMMUNICATE BY SIGN OR GESTURE, BEN GRIMM THRASHES ABOUT THE STORE...

IT'S THE THING!

HE IS PERHAPS ONLY SECONDS FROM DEATH, AND HIS TERROR BUILDS TO NEAR TANGIBLE LEVELS...

DON! DO SOMETHING! HE'S... HE'S DROWNING!

DROWNING... YEAH... HE'S... I MEAN... I GOTTA... GOTTA... OH, CRIPES, WHAT CAN I DO? WHAT CAN...

OH, FOR HEAVEN'S SAKE, DON! GIVE ME THAT SCUBA TANK!

SHE ACTS WITHOUT THOUGHT OF THE DANGER IN WHICH SHE PLACES HERSELF, THRUSTING THE LIFEBRINGING AIRHOSE INTO THE THING'S WATER PRISON...

HUHHHH!

THEN, AS THE THING DRINKS DEEP OF THE SWEETEST AIR HE CAN REMEMBER...

...THE BUBBLE OF WATER SLUICES OFF HIS ROCKY FORM, TO REVEAL...

EXCELLENT, BEN GRIMM, YOU ARE MORE RESOURCEFUL THAN I HAD BEEN TOLD.

SO LONG AS YOU POSSESS THAT AIR-TANK I CANNOT HARM YOU... BUT I CAN DO...

...THIS!

HOLEE....!

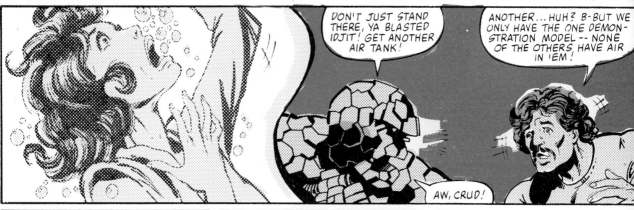

DON'T JUST STAND THERE, YA BLASTED IDJIT! GET ANOTHER AIR TANK!

ANOTHER... HUH? B-BUT WE ONLY HAVE THE ONE DEMONSTRATION MODEL -- NONE OF THE OTHERS HAVE AIR IN 'EM!

AW, CRUD!

HE HAS TWO CHOICES -- SURRENDER HIS AIR-TANK TO SAVE THE WOMAN, OR STAND BY HELPLESSLY AND WATCH HIS RESCUER DROWN.

FOR BEN GRIMM THAT IS NO CHOICE AT ALL...

OKAY, WATER-BOY... MAKE YER BLASTED MOVE!

AS YOU WISH...

HERE WE GO AGAIN!

BUT...

WHAT...?!?

HUH?

40

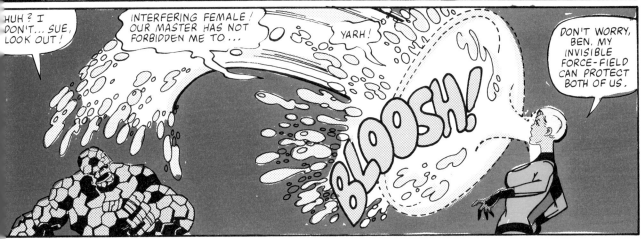

THAT'S IT? ONE PUNCH AND IT TURNS INTA MY AUNT PETUNIA'S ROCK GARDEN?

BOY, THEY SURE AIN'T BUILDING ROCK MONSTERS THE WAY THEY USED TA!

OVER-CONFIDENT OAF!

IT WILL TAKE MORE THAN YOUR PUNY STRENGTH TO DEFEAT ME!

UNGH!

POW!

AND, AS THE EARTH ELEMENTAL PRESSES ITS ADVANTAGE ON THE STUNNED THING.

...NOT FAR AWAY, OTHER EYES WITNESS THE CONFRONTATION...

THERE'S BEN. BUT IT'S THE ROCK CREATURE HE'S FIGHTING. THAT SHOULD HAVE GONE AFTER SUE!

COULD I HAVE GUESSED WRONG? IS IT POSSIBLE THAT...

NO-- THERE'S SUE IN THAT SPORTING GOODS STORE. AND THE FLOOR BEHIND HER LOOKS WET...

MY ASSUMPTION WAS CORRECT. SUE MUST HAVE LURED THE ROCK CREATURE HERE SO BEN COULD TAKE CARE OF IT.

AND IF MY OTHER ASSUMPTIONS ARE CORRECT, THAT PORTABLE GENERATOR IS JUST THE THING TO DEAL WITH THE WATER ELEMENTAL.

THESE ARE HARDLY IDEAL LABORATORY CONDITIONS, BUT UNLESS I'M MISTAKEN, THESE TWO LIVE WIRES SHOULD DO THE TRICK.

IF NOT--!

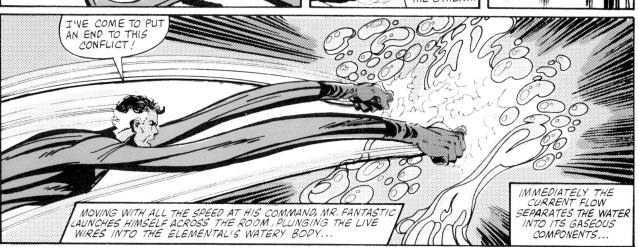

43

GONE WITHOUT A TRACE! MY HYPOTHESIS WAS CORRECT!

MY ARMS WILL BE TINGLING FOR HOURS, BUT MY UNIFORM INSULATED ME FROM THE WORST OF THE CURRENT, AND MY CRUDE ELECTROLYSIS DESTROYED THE ENTITY BY BREAKING IT DOWN INTO HYDROGEN AND OXYGEN, ALTERING IT FROM LIQUID TO GASES.

AND I THINK THIS ALSO CONFIRMS MY GUESS AS TO WHO IS BEHIND THIS ASSAULT.

BUT I CAN WORRY ABOUT THAT LATER.

BEN! BEN, CAN YOU HEAR ME? THE KEY IS TRANSMUTATION. WE HAVE TO FORCE THEM TO CHANGE THEIR STATE OF MATTER!

I HEAR YA, BIG-BRAIN...

AND IT'S MUSIC TO MY SHELL-LIKE EARS.

NOW HOLD THAT POSE FER A SECOND, ROCKY, 'CAUSE IF I'VE GOT MY BIG ORANGE MITT ON THE RIGHT PIPE...

NO!

...YOU'RE IN FER A BATH!

AND, AS THE BLASTING WATER SOFTENS THE ELEMENTAL'S EARTHEN FORM TO LIQUID MUD...

NOOOOOOO

HOLY SPIT! IT'S DISAPPEARIN'! YOU DIDN'T TELL ME I WUZ GONNA KILL THE CRITTER!

YOU DIDN'T, BEN. NOW, SUE, WE HAVE TO CHANGE THE STATE OF YOUR CAPTIVE AIR-ELEMENTAL.

BUT-- HOW? WHAT CAN I DO TO CHANGE THE STATE OF... AIR?

AIR IS A GAS, SUE, AND LIKE ANY GAS IT WILL REACT TO PRESSURE!

44

"...TRANSMUTATION CANNOT BE USED AGAINST THAT ENTITY.

"THE TORCH IS ON HIS OWN!"

HEY, SMOKEY, HOW MUCH LONGER UNTIL I SEE HOW TOUGH YOU ARE?

SO FAR YOU'VE BEEN A REAL BORE!

INSOLENT YOUNG PUP! MY MASTER'S COMMANDS MUST NOW TAKE SECOND PLACE!

IT IS TIME YOU WERE TAUGHT A LESSON!

YEOW!

I...I FELT THAT! HIS FLAME IS SO MUCH MORE INTENSE THAN MINE!

THAT'S IT, JOHN STORM! WASTE EVEN MORE OF YOUR PUNY FLAME IN USELESS FLIGHT.

IN A MOMENT I SHALL SNUFF YOU OUT LIKE AN OBSOLETE CANDLE.

AND HE CAN DO IT TOO! I DON'T KNOW HOW MUCH LONGER I CAN KEEP DODG...

NO! HE'S TRAPPED ME IN SHRINKING BANDS OF FLAME! THE...THE HEAT! I'VE NEVER FELT ANYTHING LIKE IT!

NOW IS THE HOUR OF YOUR DEATH, STORM. YOU MERELY GENERATE A FLAMING PLASMA...

...WHILE I AM THE LIVING EMBODIMENT OF ALL THAT IS FIRE. I AM FLAME!

HE IS FLAME?

THAT'S IT! THAT'S GOTTA BE IT! BUT I'VE GOTTA GET HIGHER-- HIGH ENOUGH...

...TO USE MY NOVA FLAME!

A MILE ABOVE THE CITY THE TORCH HALTS, SUDDENLY CHANNELING EVERY IOTA OF HIS POWER INTO A SINGLE BURST...

A BURST THAT RIVALS THE ENERGIES OF AN EXPLODING STAR!

FOOL! NO DEGREE OF HEAT OR FLAME CAN HARM ME! I AM INVINCIBLE!

I-- WOULDN'T-- BET-- ON --THAT-- WISE-- GUY!

HOTTER AND HOTTER BURNS THE TORCH'S FLAME...

..AS A MILES-WIDE BALL OF FIRE EXPLODES OVER THE STARTLED CITY BELOW.

AND, WHEN THE FIREBALL SHRINKS AWAY, THE TORCH IS ALONE...

AND FALLING...

MY FLAME IS ALMOST EXHAUSTED, BUT... IT WORKED! MY NOVA FLARE CONSUMED ALL THE OXYGEN FOR A MILE AROUND.

WITHOUT OXYGEN TO FEED HIS FLAME, THE ELEMENTAL BURNED HIMSELF OUT...

NOW ALL I HAVE TO DO IS SAVE MY OWN SKIN...!

GOT TO KEEP AFLAME ...JUST ENOUGH TO GUIDE MY FALL...

SPLASH!

...INTO THE RIVER!

DID IT! NOW IF I CAN JUST CATCH THE ATTENTION OF THE CREW OF THAT HANDY TUG...

HEY YOU GUYS! ONE WET MEMBER OF THE F.F. IN NEED OF A LIFT HOME!

LOOKIT! I WAS RIGHT! IT IS THE HUMAN TORCH!

HOLY COW! THE WIFE'LL NEVER BELIEVE IT!

TWENTY MINUTES LATER IN THE RESIDENTIAL LEVEL OF THE F.F.'S HQ...

THAT WAS THE TORCH. HE'S ALRIGHT, SUE. A TUG JUST FISHED HIM OUT OF THE EAST RIVER.

THEN HE MUST HAVE DEFEATED THE FLAME CREATURE WITHOUT OUR HELP!

SPEAKIN' OF WHICH, YOU OWE US A BUNCH OF EXPLANATIONS, STRETCHO!

I KNOW, BEN. FROM THE ACTIONS AND SPEECH OF THE ENTITIES, I DEDUCED THEY WERE PRIMAL ELEMENTALS. AND, ASIDE FROM DOCTOR DOOM, WHO WOULD NEVER RESORT TO SUCH CRUDE METHODS, WE HAVE ONLY ONE FOE WHO WOULD USE ALCHEMY AGAINST US.

ALCHEMY? YOU MEAN DIABLO? YOU'VE SLIPPED A COG, REED. HE'S DEAD! I SAW HIM DIE IN A SOLAR FURNACE.

YOU SAW NO BODY, BEN. AND DIABLO HAS ESCAPED "CERTAIN DEATH" BEFORE, REMEMBER?

BUT, REED, IF IT IS DIABLO, HOW CAN WE FIND HIM? HE COULD BE ANYWHERE IN THE CITY. EVEN ANYWHERE IN THE WORLD!

PERHAPS, SUE, AND I DON'T HAVE THE EQUIPMENT TO TRACE MYSTICAL ENERGIES. BUT I THINK WE KNOW SOMEONE WHO CAN LEND US A HAND...

SO, AS A CLEAR SPRING NIGHT ENFOLDS THE CITY...

I CAN WAIT NO LONGER. MY ELEMENTALS ARE LONG OVERDUE TO RETURN.

BUT I STILL POSSESS THE STATUETTES. THERE WILL COME ANOTHER TIME...

OR, WILL THERE? JUST A MOMENT, MY FRIEND. YOU SURELY WEREN'T THINKING OF LEAVING US?

WHAT?!

I'M AFRAID WE CAN'T ALLOW YOU TO WANDER OFF JUST YET, DIABLO. THERE ARE SOME SMALL MATTERS YOU SHOULD DISCUSS WITH THE POLICE FIRST...

MISTER FANTASTIC! YOU'VE FOUND ME! BUT IT DOES NOT MATTER. YOU CANNOT CONNECT ME WITH ANY CRIMES AGAINST YOU!

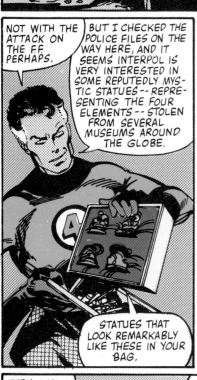

NOT WITH THE ATTACK ON THE F.F. PERHAPS.

BUT I CHECKED THE POLICE FILES ON THE WAY HERE, AND IT SEEMS INTERPOL IS VERY INTERESTED IN SOME REPUTEDLY MYSTIC STATUES -- REPRESENTING THE FOUR ELEMENTS -- STOLEN FROM SEVERAL MUSEUMS AROUND THE GLOBE.

STATUES THAT LOOK REMARKABLY LIKE THESE IN YOUR BAG.

YOU... YOU CAN'T POSSIBLY MEAN...

THE CHARGE WOULD BE POSSESSION AND TRANSPORTATION OF STOLEN PROPERTY. AND PROBABLY GRAND THEFT, TOO. THAT SHOULD SEE YOU BEHIND BARS FOR SEVERAL YEARS!

OH, THE IGNOMINITY! BUT, AT LEAST TELL ME HOW YOU FOUND ME?

AS I BELIEVE A POPULAR SONG ONCE HAD IT, DIABLO, WE HAD A "LITTLE HELP FROM OUR FRIENDS."

A VERY SPECIAL FRIEND, A MASTER OF THE MYSTIC ARTS IN FACT, CALLED DR. STRANGE!

MY PLEASURE, PROFESSOR RICHARDS. I AM EVER PREPARED TO AID THE FANTASTIC FOUR.

THEN, WE'LL TAKE OUR GUEST, AND DEPART.

THANKS AGAIN, DOC. ANYTIME WE CAN DO YOU A FAVOR JUST ASK!

THAT I SHALL, BEN GRIMM!

THO'TIS RARE THAT OUR PATHS CROSS IN THIS FASHION, IN OUR SEPARATE WAYS WE BOTH BATTLE A COMMON FOE.

NOR SHALL THAT BATTLE TRULY END, SO LONG AS MEN LIKE DIABLO SEEK TO TURN THE WORLD'S NATURAL ORDER TO THEIR OWN EVIL PURPOSES!

SUPERHERO SUPER QUIZ

Have you got the BRAIN POWER to be a super hero? Here are some simple questions about super heroes for you. All the answers can be found in the stories in this annual if you have read it carefully.

1. What is Spider-man's real name?
2. How did the Fantastic Four get their powers?
3. What is the name of the missing leader of the X-Men?
4. What is the Hulk's real name?
5. What country does Colossus come from?

6. Where do Hulk and Wolverine fight in the story in this annual?
7. Where does Aunt May work?
8. Which X-Man is incredibly lucky in a fight?

9. What is The Thing's favourite battle cry?
10. Who is the newest super hero in this book to join the ranks of MARVEL SUPERHEROES?

Think, you got them all? Check out the answers on Page 92!

49

THE UNCANNY X-MEN

The X-MEN today have a very different membership to the group of teenagers who formed the first mutant superhero team many years ago! At the moment it consists of COLOSSUS (who you can learn more about on the next page), WOLVERINE, ROGUE, PSYLOCKE, HAVOK, LONGSHOT, DAZZLER and STORM. All of them have special mutant talents that make them a powerful force for good.

But the mutant X-MEN do not just have to face the perils of super-villains. Their natural powers make them feared by many ordinary humans, and distrusted by many more. This is not helped by the savage tales of WOLVERINE with his adamantium claws, or the fact that ROGUE, who absorbs the super powers of others by touch, was once a supervillain herself! Not many people believe she has changed for the better. HAVOK is one of the oldest X-MEN, but has only recently rejoined the team, and PSYLOCKE, the telepath, and lucky LONGSHOT, are very new members. Very little is known about them.

DAZZLER is the most famous X-MEN to the general public as, in her real identity, she is the wonderful singer Alison Blaire. Hatred of her mutant powers — which turn sound to light and laser energy — forced her to give up her singing career. COLOSSUS, who can become organic steel at will, finds that being a mutant causes him great sorrow in this next story ...

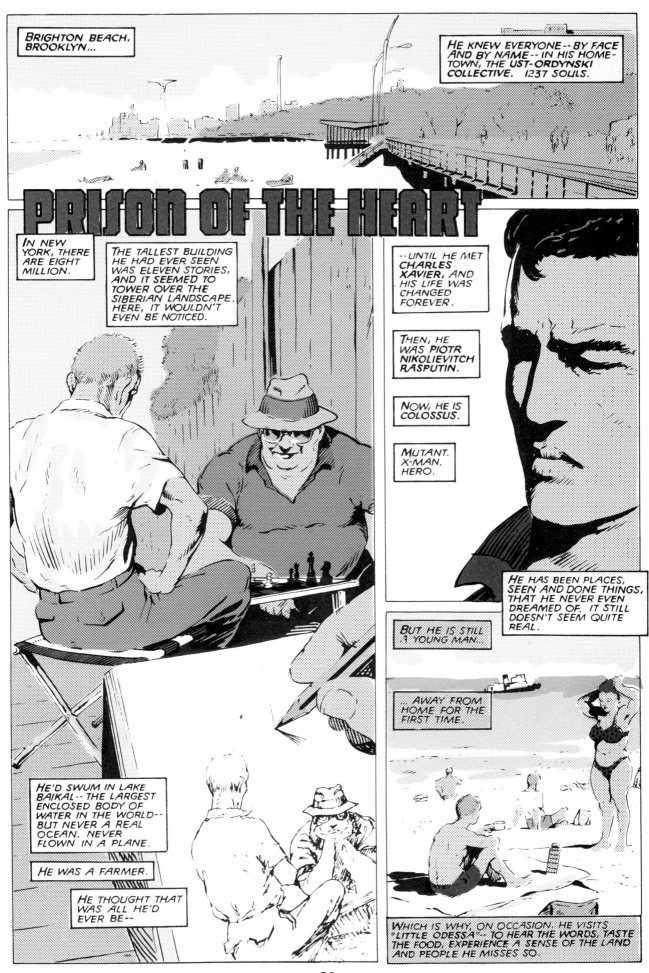

BRIGHTON BEACH, BROOKLYN...

HE KNEW EVERYONE -- BY FACE AND BY NAME -- IN HIS HOMETOWN, THE UST-ORDYNSKI COLLECTIVE. 1237 SOULS.

PRISON OF THE HEART

IN NEW YORK, THERE ARE EIGHT MILLION.

THE TALLEST BUILDING HE HAD EVER SEEN WAS ELEVEN STORIES, AND IT SEEMED TO TOWER OVER THE SIBERIAN LANDSCAPE. HERE, IT WOULDN'T EVEN BE NOTICED.

--UNTIL HE MET CHARLES XAVIER, AND HIS LIFE WAS CHANGED FOREVER.

THEN, HE WAS PIOTR NIKOLIEVITCH RASPUTIN.

NOW, HE IS COLOSSUS.

MUTANT. X-MAN. HERO.

HE HAS BEEN PLACES, SEEN AND DONE THINGS, THAT HE NEVER EVEN DREAMED OF. IT STILL DOESN'T SEEM QUITE REAL.

BUT HE IS STILL A YOUNG MAN...

HE'D SWUM IN LAKE BAIKAL -- THE LARGEST ENCLOSED BODY OF WATER IN THE WORLD-- BUT NEVER A REAL OCEAN. NEVER FLOWN IN A PLANE.

HE WAS A FARMER.

HE THOUGHT THAT WAS ALL HE'D EVER BE--

...AWAY FROM HOME FOR THE FIRST TIME.

WHICH IS WHY, ON OCCASION, HE VISITS "LITTLE ODESSA"-- TO HEAR THE WORDS, TASTE THE FOOD, EXPERIENCE A SENSE OF THE LAND AND PEOPLE HE MISSES SO.

BETTER, I THINK... ...SHE NOT FIND OUT.

SHE LOOKS AS YOUNG AS ME.

AND SO BEAUTIFUL!

SHE'S WAKING UP!

〈ARE YOU ALL RIGHT, MISS?〉

〈GET AWAY FROM ME! LEAVE ME ALONE! I WON'T GO WITH YOU-- OH?!?〉

〈YOU-- YOU'RE NOT ONE OF THEM!〉

〈DON'T BE AFRAID. YOUR ABDUCTORS HAVE RUN AWAY.〉

〈YOU'RE SAFE NOW.〉

〈YOU... SAVED ME?〉

〈YOU NEEDED HELP. I GAVE IT.〉

NICE SET'A MOVES, FELLA. YOU DONE REAL FINE!

TOO BAD, THOUGH, YOU DIDN'T NAIL THOSE BUMS...

...ALONG WIT' DERE WHEELS.

AFTER MAKING SURE THE YOUNG LADY IS UNHURT, AND GIVING HIS STATEMENT TO THE POLICE, PETER RETURNS TO THE BOARDWALK...

HERE'S YOUR BAG.

FIGURED YOU'D BE BACK FOR IT.

SPACEEBA, TOVARISCH.

TOOK A PEEK AT THE PIX. HOPE YOU DON'T MIND.

THEY ARE NOT VERY GOOD.

THE HECK YOU SAY! YOU'VE A REAL TALENT!

IT IS NOTHING. I SKETCH FOR MY LITTLE SISTER, ILLYANA, AT HOME.

MY PENCIL CAN CREATE FAR BETTER PICTURES OF THIS LAND...

...THAN MY POOR WORDS.

SHE'S A LUCKY GIRL.

SO AM I. IN ALL THE CONFUSION, WE WERE NOT INTRODUCED.

I AM *ANYA MAKAROVA*.

PIOTR RASPUTIN.

I NEVER THANKED YOU.

THERE IS NO NEED.

WHO WERE THOSE MEN? WHY DID THEY ATTACK YOU?

IN AMERICA, CRIMINALS DO NOT SEEM TO NEED...

... A REASON.

Oh.

SHE'S HIDING SOMETHING...

... BUT THAT IS HER BUSINESS.

I WAS GLAD TO HELP.

I AM AFRAID IT IS LATE. I MUST BE RETURNING HOME.

Oh, *NO!* YOU CAN'T LEAVE ME! YOU *MUSTN'T!* NOT TO-NIGHT!

???

YOU ARE A *DANCER.*

HOWEVER DID YOU GUESS?

I WAS THE YOUNGEST *PRIMA BALLERINA* IN THE HISTORY OF THE *KIROV BALLET.*

I HAVE COME TO NEW YORK FOR THE *FREEDOM* TO DANCE TO THE FULLEST EXTENT OF MY TALENT-- IN A WAY I *NEVER* COULD IN LENINGRAD.

YOU *DEFECTED?!*

NO!

NOT LIKE THAT, NOT THE WAY YOU MEAN.

IN RUSSIA, MY HEART WAS IN A CAGE.

I HAD SUCH FEELINGS, SUCH YEARNINGS-- SUCH *GLORY*-- WITHIN ME...

...WITHOUT ANY MEANS TO GIVE THEM VOICE.

AN ARTIST-- --A *TRUE* ARTIST--

--CANNOT BE TOLD HOW AND WHEN AND WHERE TO PERFORM.

RUMBLE

56

I MUST FOLLOW THE LIGHT OF MY HEART... ...WHEREVER IT LEADS-- OH!?!

CAREFUL! OR IT MAY LEAD YOU TO DISASTER.

IMPOSSIBLE! IT CANNOT LIE! IT LOOKS INTO ANOTHER'S HEART...

...AND TELLS ME WHO IS TRUE.

TONIGHT, I MAKE MY DEBUT. AND IF ALL GOES WELL, MY FUTURE IS ASSURED.

AND THAT IS WHAT YOU WANT?

OF COURSE. WHY ELSE AM I HERE?

ANYA, YOU MAY NEVER BE ABLE TO RETURN HOME!

THE WORLD IS MY HOME.

BESIDES, PIOTR NIKOLIEVITCH, YOU ARE ONE TO TALK.

HOW IS IT YOU ARE IN AMERICA?

I... AM A STUDENT.

YOUR PARENTS APPROVE?

YES.

YOU ARE LUCKY. MY FATHER SENT THOSE MEN TO DRAG ME BACK TO MY CAGE. HE NEVER UNDERSTOOD MY HEART. I DON'T EITHER, SOMETIMES.

I LOVE HIM. BUT I'M GLAD MY LEAVING HURT HIM.

MY HEART IS THE STERNEST OF TASKMASTERS. IT SAID, "DEFECT," AND I DID. IT WHISPERED, "PLAY HOOKEY," TODAY, WHEN I SHOULD BE PRACTICING OR RESTING.

IT TELLS ME TO SIT CLOSE TO YOU, TRUST YOU-- THOUGH WE HARDLY KNOW EACH OTHER.

I AM TRUE, THEN?

OH, YES.

MY CHAMPION. MY HERO.

LINCOLN CENTRE FOR THE PERFORMING ARTS.

THE METROPOLITAN OPERA HOUSE.

57

THE SEASON PREMIERE OF THE RENOWNED HANDEL COMPANY...

...A NEW BALLET...

...THEIR NEWEST STAR!

BRAVO!

ENCORE!

BRAVA!

58

SHE TELLS HIM TO WAIT, SAYING SHE'LL BE BUT A MINUTE--CHANGED AND ON HER WAY, QUICK AS SHE CAN.

AN HOUR PASSES.

STAG

TWO.

UNTIL, AT LAST...

SHTO--!?!

ANYA?!?

I WANTED TO LOOK MY BEST FOR YOU.

IT'S BEEN AGES, PETER, I KNOW, I'M SO SORRY, I COULDN'T GET AWAY.

THAT'S ALL RIGHT, I DON'T MIND.

AREN'T THESE *LOVELY?!* I'VE ENOUGH IN MY DRESSING ROOM...

...TO OPEN A FLORIST'S SHOP!

I'VE SOMETHING TO ADD TO YOUR COLLECTION.

FROM MY HEART TO YOURS.

AND HERE, MY BEAR...

...A KEEP-SAKE IN RETURN.

THIS IS VERY SUDDEN.

THINGS ARE HAPPENING SO FAST.

PERHAPS TOO FAST?

I KNOW.

I DON'T CARE.

HOME AGAIN, MY BEAR.

GOODNESS-- WE'VE WALKED THE ENTIRE NIGHT AWAY, ALL THE WAY BACK TO BROOKLYN!

WILL YOU STAY WITH ME, PIOTR NIKOLIEVITCH-- TODAY AND TOMORROW AND FOREVER AFTER ALL THE REST OF THE DAYS OF OUR LIVES?!

< DON'T MAKE PROMISES YOU CAN'T KEEP, COMRADE. >

< JUST AS YOU, ANYA MAKAROVA, SHOULDN'T ASK THE IMPOSSIBLE. >

< WHO ARE YOU?! >

< WHAT DO YOU WANT?! >

< SAME AS BEFORE. >

< WITHOUT ANY TROUBLE. >

< LEAVE ANYA ALONE! >

< GO NOW-- >

< --WHILE YOU STILL CAN! >

< I ASKED. NICELY. >

< NOW, WE TAKE! >

GASP?!!?

< DIDN'T YESTERDAY TEACH YOU BULLIES ANYTHING?! >

< I DON'T BELIEVE IT! >

< I-- I THOUGHT RYSKOV AND DMYATIN WERE DRUNK, OR LYING! >

61

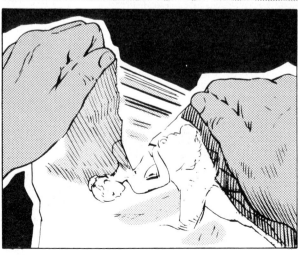

Not all superheroes get on as well as SPIDERMAN AND HIS AMAZING FRIENDS or THE FANTASTIC FOUR! Take a look at this story when WOLVERINE of THE UNCANNY X-MEN is interrupted on a perilous mission to Dallas by the recently transformed GREY skinned HULK! (His skin colour changed from green to grey as the result of more gamma radiation experiments by the Hulk's alter-ego, Doctor Bruce Banner!)

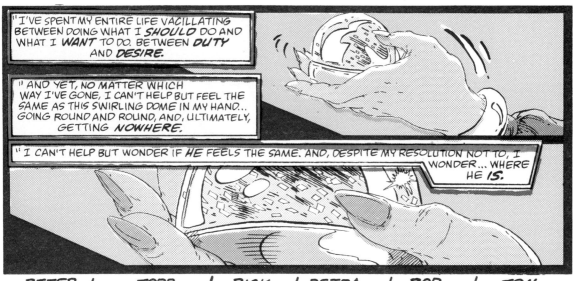

"I'VE SPENT MY ENTIRE LIFE VACILLATING BETWEEN DOING WHAT I *SHOULD* DO AND WHAT I *WANT* TO DO. BETWEEN *DUTY* AND *DESIRE*.

"AND YET, NO MATTER WHICH WAY I'VE GONE, I CAN'T HELP BUT FEEL THE SAME AS THIS SWIRLING DOME IN MY HAND... GOING ROUND AND ROUND, AND, ULTIMATELY, GETTING *NOWHERE*.

"I CAN'T HELP BUT WONDER IF *HE* FEELS THE SAME. AND, DESPITE MY RESOLUTION NOT TO, I WONDER... WHERE HE *IS*.

| PETER DAVID STORY | TODD McFARLANE ART | RICK PARKER LETTERING | PETRA SCOTESE COLOURS | BOB HARRAS EDITOR | TOM DE FALCO EDITOR IN CHIEF |

Y'KNOW, I DON'T KNOW WHERE WE ARE, BUT I'M STARTING TO THINK WE'RE GOING IN *CIRCLES*.

VICIOUS CIRCLE

YOU'RE DEAD RIGHT, RICK-O. WE TOOK A WRONG *EXIT* SOMEWHERE. WE'RE NEAR DALLAS/FORT WORTH AIRPORT, BUT OTHER THAN THAT I'M NOT *SURE*.

THIS WEIRD, INTENSE WEATHER... BLOTTING OUT EVERY TRACE OF MOON-LIGHT... IT'S MAKING THE HULK EVEN NASTIER THAN *USUAL*. IF SOMEBODY PROVOKES HIM WHEN HE'S LIKE THIS...

YEAH? WELL, THERE'S SOME-THING *I'M* SURE OF, QUARTERMAIN. I WANT *OUT!*

UH, HULK, MAYBE THAT'S *NOT* SUCH A HOT IDEA--

I SAID I WANT *OUT.*

MAYBE A BREATH OF FRESH *AIR* WOULD DO US ALL SOME *GOOD*.

CLAY! WHAT IF HE TAKES OFF AND DOESN'T COME BACK?

WHAT IF WE TRY TO STOP HIM AND HE KILLS US?

KLIK

GOOD POINT.

64

PAN AM FLIGHT #134, THIS IS D/FW. I SUGGEST YOU REROUTE TO HOUSTON AS WE ARE STILL **SNOWED-IN** HERE.

PHIL, THIS SNOW'S PLAYING HAVOC WITH OUR RADAR, BUT I **THINK** I'VE GOT **ANOTHER** PLANE ENTERING OUR AIRSPACE.

OH, THAT'S **GREAT**. SOME JET-JOCKEY JOY-RIDING, I'LL BET.

UNIDENTIFIED AIRCRAFT, YOU HAVE ENTERED THE AIRSPACE OF DALLAS/FORT WORTH AIRPORT. YOU MUST DEPART IMMEDIATELY AS YOU ARE CREATING A SERIOUS HAZARD TO OTHER AIRCRAFT.

WE DON'T **CREATE** HAZARDS, BUB. WE **STOP** THEM.

THIS IS THE TOWER, PLEASE IDENTIFY YOURSELF.

AND INSIDE THE MYSTERIOUS BLACKBIRD...

...SIX INDIVIDUALS ARE GATHERED-- THE CURRENT MEMBERS OF THE OUTLAW MUTANT BAND KNOWN AS THE **X-MEN**.

TOWER, YOU WOULDN'T BELIEVE ME IF I **TOLD** YOU. BUT YOU **CAN** BELIEVE THIS...

IF YOU DON'T GIVE US CLEARANCE TO LAND, YOU'LL HAVE A LOT BIGGER HEADACHE THAN A SNOWSTORM. CHEW ON IT FOR A MINUTE, OKAY?

65

66

HEY!

TOWER, THIS IS PAN AM 134! SOMETHING *HIT* US, A MISSILE, I DON'T *KNOW* WHAT!

WE'VE LOST OUR NUMBER ONE ENGINE, IT'S IN *FLAMES!* MAYDAY! MAYDAY!

KRUNCH

BATOOOOM!

ROGUE! I'M PICKIN' UP A *MAYDAY,* DARLIN'. COMMERCIAL JET.

AH *SEE* IT, WOLVIE. LOOKS LIKE A SHOOTING STAR!

GET *OUT* THERE, KID. RIP THE ENGINE OFF THE WING AND HELP THE PLANE TO THE GROUND. WE'LL FOLLOW.

BUT, WOLVIE-- IF I TOSS THE ENGINE AWAY, IT COULD *LAND* ON SOMEBODY.

I KNOW. BUT THERE COULD BE HUNDREDS OF PEOPLE IN THAT PLANE. THEY'LL DIE FOR *SURE* IF THAT PLANE GOES UP IN FLAMES. NOW GET GOING. ROGUE... WHEN YOU DROP THE BURNING ENGINE...

"...MAKE SURE YOU AIM FOR SOMEPLACE ON THE GROUND WITH NO LIGHTS. CHANCES ARE, IT'LL BE AN OPEN FIELD OR A LAKE.

"ANYONE DUMB ENOUGH TO BE OUT THERE ON A NIGHT LIKE *THIS*--

"-- THAT'S *THEIR* TOUGH LUCK."

GREAT. I HAVEN'T FOUND ANY FOOD, AND NOW I CAN'T EVEN FIND THE *VAN.*

THIS *STINKS.* I FEEL LIKE *HITTIN'* SOMETHIN', BUT YA CAN'T PUNCH A *SNOWFLAKE.*

HOLD IT. WHAT'S THAT *WHISTLING* SOUND? LIKE...

SOMETHING *FALLING.*

KRASH!

WAS THAT SOMEBODY'S IDEA OF A *JOKE?!*

"I'M CALLED WOLVERINE. I'M A MUTANT... LIKE THE REST OF THE X-MEN, AND AS I CHECK OVER THE WING ON THIS AIRPLANE ROGUE BROUGHT DOWN, I THINK ABOUT ALL THE *STRANGENESS* IN MY LIFE RIGHT NOW.

"THIS UNREAL WEATHER. THE LEADERSHIP OF THE X-MEN. IT'S AS IF THE WORLD'S IN *FLUX* AROUND ME. BUT MY INSTINCTS...THEY'VE BEEN A CONSTANT. UN-SWERVING, DEPENDABLE. UNTIL LATELY, MAYBE.

"IF I CAN BELIEVE MY HEIGHTENED *SENSES,* THIS WING WAS TRASHED BY THE *HULK.* BUT HIS SCENT HAS *CHANGED*...IT'S FAMILIAR, BUT DIFFERENT. I DIDN'T THINK THAT WAS POSSIBLE. I'D *LOVE* TO CHECK IT OUT, BUT I CAN'T LEAVE THE TEAM. ME, THE LONER. NOW I'M THE LEADER. FUNNY WORLD. I'M *NOT* LAUGHING.

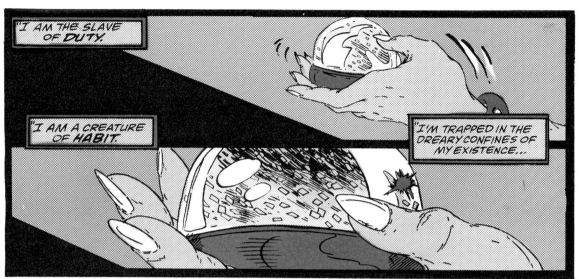

"I AM THE SLAVE OF *DUTY*.

"I AM A CREATURE OF *HABIT*.

"I'M TRAPPED IN THE DREARY CONFINES OF MY EXISTENCE...

"STALLED AND UNABLE TO GO *FORWARD*, SNOW-BLINDED AND UNABLE TO LOOK *BACK*.

"I KNOW WHAT I *SHOULD* DO, AND WHAT I *SHOULDN'T*. I ALWAYS *HAVE*, BUT IT'S NEVER HELPED.

"THE ONE THING I *SHOULDN'T* DO IS THINK ABOUT *HIM*. AND YET ONCE AGAIN, I DO.

MANUFACTURERS OF FINE MEAT PRODUCT

PATTY-TIME

INC.

EZ4U

"WHERE *IS* HE?"

HELLO IN THERE! THIS IS SERGEANT O'RILEY OF THE NATIONAL GUARD! IS ANY-BODY *IN* THERE?

WE'RE HERE TO *HELP* YOU!

AND I'M SMART ENOUGH TO KNOW THAT YOU GUYS WON'T LEAVE ME ALONE JUST BY MY *ASKING* YOU!

I HAVE TA *STEP* ON YOU, LIKE THE *BUGS* YOU ARE!

RUN!!!

THAT'S RIGHT! *RUN!* LET EVERY-BODY KNOW, THE *HULK'S* IN TOWN!

AND THE NEXT GUY WHO CROSSES ME IS GONNA GET *FRIED!*

SSSSSSSSSSS

"THE WIND CARRIES THE SMOKE TO ME BEFORE WE FINALLY *SEE* IT... SOME WOODS ARE BURNING. AND THERE'S AN APARTMENT HOUSE NEARBY.

"WE SHOULD REALLY GET OUT OF THIS PLACE... BUT PEOPLE MAY BE *TRAPPED* IN THAT BUILDING, CAN'T LET THEM DIE.

"I TELL... *MY*... TEAM TO GET TO THE APARTMENT BUILDING, EVACUATE EVERYONE, HELP WHEREVER THEY CAN. I PULL ON MY *MASK*...

71

"AND CHECK OUT THE *SOURCE* OF THE *BLAZE*. I FIND THE BURNING REMAINS OF A TRUCK. WIND CARRIED SPARKS TO THE WOODS.

I WONDER WHO THE *JERK* IS WHO'S RE-SPONSIBLE FOR THIS?

"WHATEVER HAPPENED HERE, IT'S NONE OF MY CONCERN. STILL, I SAY OUT LOUD..."

"I REALIZE LATER THAT THE WIND'S AGAINST ME. MY WORDS CARRY.

"HIS SCENT DOESN'T.

"MY ONLY HINT IS A LOW ANIMAL *GROWL* HE MAKES A SPLIT INSTANT BEFORE HE WOULD HAVE *HIT* ME. IT'S ENOUGH.

SNIKT

"I POP MY *CLAWS.*

"BUT *NOT* MY CORK.

"I DON'T *DO* THAT ANYMORE I'M *CIVILIZED* NOW.

AT LEAST, THAT'S WHAT I LIKE TO *TELL* MYSELF."

72

THEN YOU'LL DIE TODAY!

"HE MAY BE RIGHT. BUT TO DIE IN POINTLESS BATTLE WITH HIM...IT'S A *WASTE*. IT'S EVERYTHING I'VE TRIED TO PUT MYSELF *BEYOND*."

YOU THINK I'VE *FORGOTTEN* WHEN WE FIRST MET IN CANADA? I JUST WANTED TO BE LEFT *ALONE*, BUT YOU WOULDN'T BACK OFF, OH NO.

YOU HAD TO HAVE YOUR *PIECE* OF ME.

I'VE *CHANGED* SINCE THEN.

KNOWING WHEN TO FIGHT AND WHEN TO *WALK AWAY* IS MORE SMARTS THAN *YOU'LL* EVER HAVE.

SO HAVE *I*! I'VE GOTTEN SMART--

AND YOU'VE GOTTEN *GUTLESS*!

74

YOU *TALK* TOO MUCH. YOU *THINK* TOO MUCH.

BTRUNCH!

YOU'RE A SPINELESS *WIMP,* LOOKING FOR *EXCUSES* TO STAY OUT OF MY WAY!

YOU THINK YOU'RE SOMETHIN' *SPECIAL!* BUT YOU'RE *NOTHING!*

THOOM!

"THAT EAR-SPLITTING CLAP OF HIS IS *DEVAS-TATING* AGAINST SOME-ONE NORMAL.

"AGAINST *ME,* WITH MY ACUTE HEARING, IT'S ALMOST LETHAL.

"HE KEEPS *ON* ME, SHOUTING, *CURS-ING,* NOT GIVING ME TIME TO *THINK.*

"AND THEN...THOUGHT IS *GONE,* REPLACED BY FURY, ANGER, HATRED HOT AND BEAUTIFUL.

"I'M SICK OF FIGHTING *MYSELF.*

"I'M *PANTING.* EVERY MUSCLE IN MY BODY *CONTRACTS.*

"HE *WANTS* IT. *I* WANT IT.

ALL RIGHT.

"ALL RIGHT.

SNIKT

"HE WON.

"I STAND THERE, HOWLING MY TRIUMPH TO THE MOON I CAN'T *SEE*. BUT IN THE HEART HIDDEN BY MY HEAVING CHEST, I KNOW HE WON.

"BECAUSE HE MADE WHAT I *AM* STRONGER THAN WHAT I *THINK* I AM.

"LIKE A *WILD ANIMAL*, I RIPPED HIM APART. AND THE *WORST* THING IS...

"I'M *GLAD*.

" AND THEN... MY *INSTINCTS* TELL ME SOMETHING MY *MIND* REFUSES TO ACCEPT.

"HE'S STANDING. HE'S ALIVE.

"HE'S... ACTUALLY GETTING *ANGRIER*.

"HE'S GETTING *STRONGER*.

"AND THE GAPING WOUNDS IN HIS CHEST ARE... *HEALING*.

LET'S...

LET'S... TRY THAT... **AGAIN.**

I'M GLAD I TRIED THE **SHORTWAVE** AGAIN. I PICKED UP SOME SORT OF **POLICE** REPORT--

SOUNDS LIKE THE **HULK** AND SOMEBODY ELSE ARE SLUGGING IT OUT ON THE HIGHWAY, NEAR EXIT 12. IF WE **HURRY** WE CAN GET THERE BEFORE THEY LEVEL **DALLAS.** GOOD THING I FOUND THIS THING'S ON-BOARD GUIDANCE SYSTEM, OR WE'D'VE BEEN SNOWBOUND **FOREVER.**

THIS IS **INSANE.** WE'RE RISKING LIFE AND LIMB TO FIND THE GAMMA RAY BOMBS THE GOVERNMENT'S STOCKPILING, AND OUR GREATEST **ALLY** IS ALSO OUR BIGGEST **HANDICAP.**

HOPEFULLY STEALING THIS VAN AND RUNNING FROM **SHIELD** WILL BE WORTH IT, BUDDY. THE WORLD DOESN'T **NEED** A WEAPON THAT COULD CREATE EVEN **MORE** GAMMA GUYS FOR US TO WORRY ABOUT.

WHAT'CHA **GOT** THERE, CLAY?

SOME **PERSONAL** EFFECTS I GRABBED FROM GAMMA BASE RIGHT BEFORE I BLEW IT UP.

To Clay --

Thanks for Everything

The Banners

...IN **HAPPIER** TIMES.

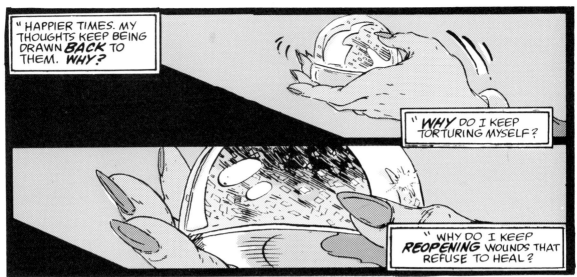

"HAPPIER TIMES. MY THOUGHTS KEEP BEING DRAWN *BACK* TO THEM. *WHY?*

"*WHY* DO I KEEP TORTURING MYSELF?"

"WHY DO I KEEP *REOPENING* WOUNDS THAT REFUSE TO HEAL?"

THOSE PIGSTICKERS OF YOURS DIDN'T STOP ME *BEFORE,* AND THEY *WON'T* HELP YA *NOW!*

"I REALIZE WHAT IS HAPPENING, AND I DON'T *LIKE* IT.

"THE MOST COMMON RESULT OF RADIATION EXPOSURE IS *CANCER* -- AN ABNORMAL GROWTH OF CELLS.

"WHEN BRUCE BANNER GOT HIT BY GAMMA RAYS, IT GAVE HIM A KIND OF CANCER, CALLED THE *HULK.*

"I CUT HIM *AGAIN* -- HE HEALS EVEN *FASTER.*

"I ALWAYS THOUGHT THE HULK'S SKIN WAS *IMPENETRABLE.* I WAS *WRONG.*

"BUT HIS CELLS REPRODUCE SO *FAST* IT *SEEMS* THAT WAY. AND THE MADDER HE GETS, THE MORE HIS SYSTEM *SPEEDS UP* THE MORE CELLS HE PRODUCES...

"HE GETS *TOUGHER. STRONGER.* HARDER TO *HURT.*

WHUMP

79

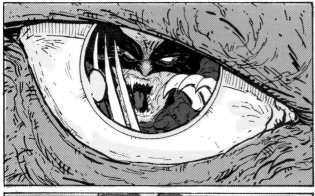

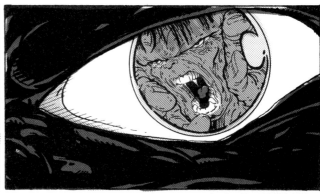

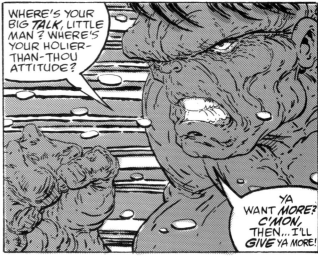

WHERE'S YOUR BIG *TALK*, LITTLE MAN? WHERE'S YOUR HOLIER-THAN-THOU ATTITUDE?

YA WANT *MORE*? C'MON, THEN... I'LL *GIVE* YA MORE!

C'MON!!

RAAARGHH!

YOU'VE ALL SPENT *YEARS* LAUGHING AT ME, TAKING *ADVANTAGE* OF ME. I WAS THE DUMB GREEN GIANT... BUT NOW I START GIVING IT ALL BACK.

EVERY *BIT* OF IT!

WHAM

GETTIN' *UP* AGAIN? *GOOD!*

I WANT THIS TO LAST A *LONG* TIME!

KRAK

ENOUGH.!!

ENOUGH! DO YOU *HEAR* ME? *ENOUGH!*

I SWEAR TO HEAVEN, I DON'T *UNDERSTAND* YOU PEOPLE! EVERY TIME TWO OF YOU MUSCLE-BOUND *BOZOS* GET TOGETHER, YOU TRY AND BEAT EACH OTHER'S *BRAINS* OUT!

OR AT LEAST WHAT *PASSES* FOR BRAINS!

I THOUGHT YOU WANTED TO FIND THE GAMMA BOMBS, HULK, HELP HEAD OFF THE CREATION OF MORE CREATURES LIKE *YOURSELF.*

AND YOU WASTE YOUR TIME BEATING UP ON *WOLVERINE!*

HAS IT OCCURRED TO YOU THAT IF *I* COULD FIND YOU, *SHIELD* COULD, TOO?

AND IF THEY FIND YOU DURING THE *DAY* WHEN YOU'RE BANNER, YOU CAN KISS YOURSELF *GOODBYE.*

IF YOU'RE NOT THE "MINDLESS" HULK ANYMORE, START *ACTING* THAT WAY. GET SOME *PRIORITIES,* FOR PITY'S SAKE!

AND *YOU! WOLVERINE!* DON'T YOU HAVE ANYTHING *BETTER* YOU SHOULD BE DOING?

"AND IN A STRANGLED VOICE I REPLY--

YEAH.

YEAH. I *DO*.

I THOUGHT I'D COME SO *FAR*. THEN I RUN INTO YOU AND *BANG*, THE YEARS FALL AWAY.

NO MATTER HOW FAR I GO, I'M RIGHT BACK WHERE I *STARTED*.

YEAH, WELL, YOU'RE JUST LIKE ALL THE *OTHERS*, WHO ALWAYS THOUGHT THEY WERE BETTER'N *ME*.

WELL, NOW I'M BETTER'N *ALL* OF YA!

UNDERSTAND ?! *ALL* OF YA!

AND I DON'T HAVE TO BEAT UP EVERY LOW-LIFE LIKE *YOU* TO PROVE IT. YOU *TELL* 'EM, SHRIMP. TELL 'EM THE HULK'S BETTER THAN *ANY* OF 'EM.

YEAH. SURE.

EXIT 292 DALLAS CITY CENTER

" I CAN'T RE-MEMBER THE LAST TIME I WANTED A *CIGAR* THIS BAD.

SO ONCE WE'RE OUT OF HERE, WHERE *TO*, CLAY? NEW ORLE-ANS, WHERE *BETTY* IS?

NO. KANSAS, WHERE MY *BROTHER*, ALAN, IS.

ALAN... QUARTERMAIN ?

WEAKLINGS. COULDN'T GET *ANYTHING* DONE WITHOUT ME.

IF I DIDN'T NEED THEM TO WATCH OUT FOR *BANNER'S* SCRAWNY HIDE...

DON'T LAUGH. HE'S THE *ELDER*. IT *COULD'VE* BEEN ME. ANYWAY, HE CAN *HELP* US FIND THE GAMMA BOMBS.

CONVINCING BRUCE THAT THE BOMBS ARE MORE IMPORTANT THAN FINDING BETTY MAY BE TOUGH.

CLAY..., YOU THINK BETTY'S BEEN THINKING ABOUT BRUCE SINCE SHE RAN OFF?

NOT IF SHE'S *SMART*, RICK-O. NOT IF SHE'S *SMART*.

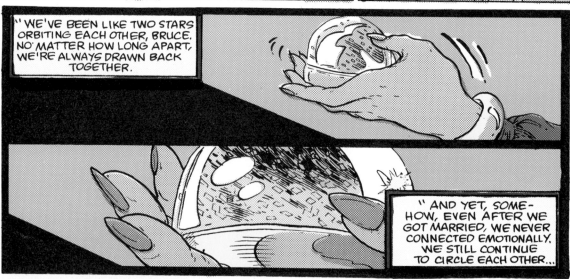

"WE'VE BEEN LIKE TWO STARS ORBITING EACH OTHER, BRUCE. NO MATTER HOW LONG APART, WE'RE ALWAYS DRAWN BACK TOGETHER.

" AND YET, SOMEHOW, EVEN AFTER WE GOT MARRIED, WE NEVER CONNECTED EMOTIONALLY. WE STILL CONTINUE TO CIRCLE EACH OTHER...

"LIKE TWO SHIPS *PASSING* IN THE NIGHT.

"AN ENDLESS, VICIOUS CIRCLE. A *CYCLE*, EVEN...

KRAK!

" A CYCLE THAT CAN ONLY BE BROKEN... AT GREAT EXPENSE."

HOW TO DRAW

THE HULK

STEP 1: A SERIES OF OVALS SHOULD DO THE TRICK AND GET YOU STARTED.

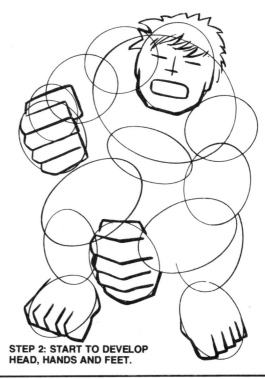

STEP 2: START TO DEVELOP HEAD, HANDS AND FEET.

STEP 3: DEVELOP FACIAL EXPRESSION, HEAVY UP LINES AROUND MUSCLES, WORK ON HANDS AND FEET.

ADD PLENTY OF MUSCLE LINES, BLACK IN HAIR AND INSIDE OF MOUTH. DEVELOP TATTERED TROUSERS.

PROLOGUE:

WHEW! MUCH AS I LIKE SPENDING A DAY WITH AUNT MAY --

--IT'D SURE BE GOOD TO GET HOME AND TAKE A NICE, LONG BATH.

HEY, ISN'T THAT--?

YUP, IT'S MY OLD BUDDY, THE THING!

HIYA, BEN! WHAT'S UP?

HOW'S THE REST OF THE FF?

UH, YOU KNOW, THE FANTASTIC FOUR?

YOUR PARTNERS?

REED? SUE?

THE TORCH?

YOO HOO--ANYONE HOME?

BEN?

86

89

THE END

SPOT THE MISTAKE! ANSWERS
from Page 25

Here's a picture of the old web slinger drawn properly for your wall! ▶

SUPER HERO QUIZ ANSWERS

NO SNEAKING a glance at this page if you haven't tried to answer our easy super hero questions on Page 49. Super heroes **NEVER** cheat! (Well, not much, anyway . . .)

1. Peter Parker, photographer.
2. They were exposed to cosmic rays.
3. Storm.
4. Bruce Banner, scientist.
5. Russia.
6. Dallas.
7. She runs her own boarding-house.
8. Longshot.
9. "It's Clobberin' Time!"
10. You are! What do you mean, you haven't written your name in the front of this book yet? (Trick question, there).

DID YOU KNOW that Spider-man's webbing only lasts for one hour? Then it evaporates!

DID YOU KNOW that Wolverine's claws are made of adamantium, the strongest metal in the world? Not even the Marvel Super hero THOR can break it with his magical URU hammer.

DID YOU KNOW that Marvel has been producing stories about super heroes for over TWENTY-FIVE years?

MARVEL

**Hope you enjoyed this year's MARVEL SUPER HEROES ANNUAL
Be sure to watch out for us on television and in your favourite Marvel Comics!**